FIRST STORY

First Story's vision is a society that encourages and supports young people from all backgrounds to practise creative writing for pleasure, self-expression and agency. We believe everyone has a unique voice, a story to tell and a right to be heard. Our flagship programme places inspiring professional writers into secondary schools, where they work intensively with students and teachers to develop young people's creativity, confidence and ability. Through our core provision and extended opportunities, including competitions and events, participants develop skills to thrive in education and beyond.

Find out more at firststory.org.uk

First Story is a registered charity number 1122939 and a private company limited by guarantee incorporated in England with number 06487410. First Story is a business name of First Story Limited.

First published 2022 by First Story Limited
44 Webber Street, Southbank, London, SE1 8QW

www.firststory.org.uk

ISBN 978-0-85748-507-6

1 3 5 7 9 10 8 6 4 2

A CIP catalogue record for this book is available from the British Library.

Printed and bound in the UK by Aquatint
Typeset by Avon DataSet Ltd
Copy-edited by Vivienne Heller
Proofread by Sally Beets
Cover designed by Antoni Rykaluk with Lucy Dove

This Book Has Swallowed Me Whole

An Anthology by the First Story Group
at Appleton Academy (Primary)

EDITED BY NICK TOCZEK | 2022

FIRST STORY

As Patron of First Story I am delighted that it continues to foster and inspire the creativity and talent of young people in secondary schools serving low-income communities.

I firmly believe that nurturing a passion for reading and writing is vital to the health of our country. I am therefore greatly encouraged to know that young people in this school – and across the country – have been meeting each week throughout the year in order to write together.

I send my warmest congratulations to everybody who is published in this anthology.

HRH The Duchess of Cornwall

Contents

Introduction

Nick Toczek, Writer-in-Residence

This primary anthology marks the end of my eighth year as a First Story Writer-in-Residence at Appleton Academy. For the past two of those years, the Covid-19 pandemic cast a shadow of uncertainty over whether this work could continue. However, we managed to complete both years and to produce the two primary anthologies. Last year's workshop sessions were all conducted virtually (via Teams) because no guests were allowed to enter the school. This year, however, I've actually been back working in the library for all of our sessions. That's been a great relief. Direct contact with the pupils makes a huge difference.

Writing is a very human process. It's about voicing your thoughts, ideas, emotions and values. To draw all of this from pupils is far from easy via a computer screen. Human contact matters. It's the difference between real friends and Facebook 'friends'. It's why homes and schools matter. Here's where we meet those who influence and educate us.

I've worked as a writer-in-schools for half a century. I love this job and you can't do it properly if you're not actually in each school. The poems and stories in this anthology are all about that very real human contact, which is why I've loved editing this collection. These pupils, like all their peers, have suffered from the severe social, academic and lifestyle deprivations imposed over the past two years by the pandemic. This book testifies to their individual and collective resilience. Their writing is all about survival, self-assurance in weathering whatever storms life throws at them. Via imaginative tales, it also tackles the subject of death, something that Covid, climate change and international conflict have made very real for all of us. However, regardless of their chosen subject, the poems and stories produced by the pupils and published in this collection are vivid, readable and impressive. And, overall, their words are confident, fun, moving, funny and inspiring.

I'm sure that you'll enjoy reading this book every bit as much as they've enjoyed writing it and I've enjoyed encouraging their creativity and self-confidence.

Huge thanks are due to the pupils and staff at Appleton, especially the school's amazing librarian, Gill Parr, with whom I'm privileged to have worked for many years. Equal gratitude is due to First Story, and particularly to their regional organiser, Andy Hill, whose unstinting support and positivity has made this whole endeavour not just possible, but a joy.

Foreword

Gill Parr, Library Manager

Creativity in the library. Our Thursday afternoon sessions have been great fun this year. It's been wonderful to get back to having Nick visit us in person and not just see him on a screen. The students have worked hard and produced some lovely pieces of work. Each piece has an individuality all of its own and our writers have embraced the writing ideas given to them. We've laughed at some funny stories, almost cried at some heartfelt writing, and swallowed screams when listening to the horror stories.

Thanks again to Nick Toczek, our Writer-in-Residence, for sharing his ideas with us, to Andy Hill, First Story Regional Manager, for his constant support, and to the students themselves for sharing their innermost thoughts.

I really hope you enjoy this book!

Ghost Fingers

Ruby Dunning

My ghost fingers are plastic,
Touching people in the night.

My ghost fingers are sweet,
Tempting children with delights.

My ghost fingers are salty,
Not enjoyed by all.

My ghost fingers pull the trigger.
Silver bullets fly.

Didn't You Know?

Georgia Bentley

Didn't you know that statues can talk?
Didn't you know that books can walk?

Didn't you know that pigs can mime?
Didn't you know that babies don't whine?

Didn't you know that mince pies cry?
Didn't you know that millionaires don't buy?

Didn't you know there is no crime?
Didn't you know that poetry doesn't rhyme?

Rules for Living

Grace Duffy

If you're reading this please carry on!

Everyone is entitled to love how they want.
Gender isn't a choice.

Skin colour doesn't define a personality.
Talk things through, understand others.

Speak out about abuse
And never bully.

It's your litter.
Take it home.

Don't be selfish.
You're not the only person on this earth.

Help the homeless.
You could be in their shoes one day.

Online Friends

Amina Ali

The two girls were friends in the virtual world. They met online, they chatted online and they grew to be close friends online. Now the time had come for them to meet in person. Would they still like each other? What would she really look like?

They checked into a hotel and met in reception; both girls wondering what the other one would really be like. Instant recognition. They were just like their profile pictures!

They wandered outside to talk and came across an old man looking lonely and lost. He didn't seem to have much and looked like he hadn't eaten all day. Both girls reached into their pockets at the same time. They really were alike!

Weather or Not

Amy Atter

Whack the clouds,
Create a downpour.

Stroke the sky,
Make a rainbow.

Tickle the sun,
Start a heatwave.

Whisper to the wind,
Force a hurricane.

Look after the planet.

That's Life

Lexi Preston

Life is amazing, everyone laughs, has a good time. Not one person is bored or boring.

Except... that's in my dreams. My generation is boring. We don't laugh, we've forgotten how to play and how to have relationships. We are a generation of chicken-nugget-eating, computer-fixated sweetie eaters!

The Truth

Sebastian Ward

We all know the Earth is flat.
We are sure that thin people are fat.

Did you realise water is dry?
Did you know that books can fly?

Everyone is certain that pigs live on the moon
And it always snows in June.

Did you know that two and two make five
Or that mummies are alive?

It's a fact that apples look like pears
And that churches don't allow prayers.

All this is the absolute truth,
I swear!

Serves Me Right

Leo Richmond

I went out onto the street thinking I was super cool. Me, my scooter and my best friend. It was a top-of-the-range scooter, and everyone thought it was great; that was until I rode over a drain, wobbled and fell off. There was a horrid tearing sound as my front tooth went through my lip. There was blood everywhere and it hurt a lot. I had to fight back tears and appear calm.

I should have known not to take it, my brother's scooter. He was sixteen, and it was a powerful thing. Lesson learnt!

Grandma's Smile

Daisy Wilkinson

Grandma's smile warms the sun.
Grandma's smile lights up the night.

Grandma's smile's a warm embrace.
Grandma's smile's so full of love.

Grandma's smile, oh so sweet.
Grandma's smile makes me complete.

The Knock

Zakim Hanif-Thompson

Three loud knocks woke me up again, for the third time that week. My mum answered the door, hoping it would just be the postman. No, the police yet again, an armed officer pointing a gun at her head.

'Do you have anything on you?' he shouted.

'No,' she replied with confidence.

My heart had missed a beat and was slowly reverting to its normal rate.

'Why does our skin colour make us not safe?' I asked.

A Better Earth

Amy Ortola

A better earth would have no more littering.
A better earth would have no more polluting.
A better earth would involve no cutting down of trees.

A better earth would have no more racism.
A better earth would have no more sexism.
A better earth would make room for the homeless.

A better earth would have no more bullying.
A better earth would have no more crime.
A better earth would befriend the friendless.

A better earth would be spectacular!

A Letter to the World

Heidi Hargreaves

Hey everyone…

Stop littering. Animals are dying. Coral is fading. How about cutting down your use of plastic? It's strangling the environment.

Don't get me started on homelessness. How much money do those in the Government have whilst people are sleeping on the streets? Think about how we spend our money!

Food needs to be cheaper. Nobody should go to school hungry.

Don't put up with bullying. Tell your teacher. Tell someone. And remember, it doesn't matter who you love as long as you're happy.

Finally, don't put up with racism as everyone matters.

Please take this in, and try to make a change.

The Truth

Oscar Wang

We all know that water is dry.
We all know that paintings cry.

We all know that fish can walk.
We all know that flowers talk.

We all know that the moon is dark.
We all know that elephants bark.

We all know that chairs can dance.
We all know that I'm taking a chance!

Welcome to Hell

William Walker

A gloomy orange glow seeped under the bed. The skinny, pale creature crawled out, jagged bones creaking, its dislocated arms sticking out at an odd angle. Long, bony fingers pointed at the terrified boy, hiding under the covers.

The creature rasped, 'Come with me. He is waiting for you.'

Manifesto for Change

Joel Brown

Suicide is terrible,
Drugs are too.
Abuse is unforgivable,
Kidnapping is the pits!

Once I am in charge the world will be a better place.
I will listen to all people who wish to talk,
And help those in poverty,
To make a fair and better place.

Reverse climate change,
Care for the planet.
End this stream of selfishness,
To make a brighter future.

Man Steals Child

Zoe Makhubelo

On January 19th this year, the police received a call from a terrified mother of one.

'Police, what's your emergency?'

'There's a man,' she screamed. 'He's taken my child.'

'Can you describe him?'

'He's tall and dressed all in black.'

'Are you hurt?'

'No but he's got my baby!'

'We'll be right there.'

When the police arrived, the woman was huddled in a corner, terrified. The man and child were nowhere to be seen.

Dear Mr Wyke*

Isaac Kuyateh

You are amazing,
But why you always wear that jacket I will never know.
You make me start gazing,
Looking to my future, a world of the unknown.

Thank you for the corner shops,
The honey and the pickle.
If you could talk, I think you'd say,
'Let's go get a McDonald's.'

Mr Wyke, will I ever earn enough money
To take me away from here,
See the world
    But remember my beginnings?

Wyke is the district in Bradford where Appleton Academy is located.

Mistaken Identity

Liam Woods

It was shortly after 9 p.m., and the man had just put his children to bed. He was happily getting ready to sit down with his wife and watch *The Chase*. His favourite time of night.

The sounds from outside seemed to get closer, loud banging noises and far-off shouts. As they got nearer, the couple realised that it was the police.

They looked out of their living-room window and were surprised to see a group of police cars and armed police rushing towards their door.

'This is the police. We need to talk to you.'

They opened the door and let them in. Wrong house!

We Know

Preston Simpson

We know that pigs can fly,
That tall people are shy.

We know that teachers always wear ties,
That Alexas are spies.

We know that vampires love light,
That bats hate the night.

We know that rabbits can't bite,
That children never fight.

Gunshots

Scarlett Oeser

Class of 2010 were on their way to the auditorium. It was the last day of school. You could hear the echo of their footsteps along the silent corridors. The whole school was crammed into the one room.

Suddenly an ear-splitting siren broke out making everyone cover their ears. The students were scared. What had happened to cause the siren to go off? The students looked around at each other.

Loud gunshots rang around the room. Pupils screamed and lights flickered. Some students reached for their phones.

It was then that the teacher noticed one student was missing.

Seven Six-Word Stories

Blind man robs house. His house!
William Walker

Found love. He was a killer.
Georgia Bentley

A book has swallowed me whole.*
Scarlett Oeser

Seven billion people dead, earth doomed.
Sebastian Ward

Lights twitching, doors creaking… haunted school.
Amina Ali

Face in the painting disappeared again.
Daisy Wilkinson

Talented footballer scored his last goal.
Leo Richmond

* *This gave us the title of our book. Thanks, Scarlett!*

As

Zakim Hanif-Thompson, Heidi Hargreaves and Preston Simpson

As silky as hair,
As hard as a stare.
As lasting as love,
As graceful as a dove.
As difficult as dying,
As fantastic as flying.
As comfy as a chair,
As deadly as a grizzly bear.
As silent as the night,
As essential as sight.
As huge as fame,
As embarrassing as the walk of shame.
As strong as God,
As tiny as peas in a pod.

A Strange Encounter

Isaac Kuyateh

It was me, standing there all alone. I was waiting for my taxi to take me home. The night was dark and scary. I never could get used to waiting alone in the dark. Why was the taxi taking so long? I caught the outline of a figure watching me from across the road. What did it want? I shoved my hands in my pockets and hoped that the taxi wouldn't be long.

'I'll see you in the future,' a voice whispered.

I got into my taxi and sighed.

I Don't Like School

Leo Richmond

No more teachers,
'Cos I don't like school.

No more classrooms,
'Cos I don't like school.

No more learning,
'Cos I don't like school.

No more maths,
'Cos I don't like school.

No more English,
'Cos I don't like school.

School holidays.
I'll be bored.
Yeah!

James

William Walker

The karate training camp is halfway up a snowy mountain and James trains there every day with his sensei. He hates training and has a plan to run away. He tells no one and keeps up the training until he is ready to leave. All he takes with him is himself and his desire to run.

Travelling across countries, he ends up in London with no money and nowhere to go. He is set upon by a group of teenagers who push him to the ground, expecting to beat him easily. James fights back and beats them. He makes a life for himself and becomes unrecognisable from the boy attacked on the streets of London.

Gradually the pull of life in the countryside overtakes him and he returns to the snowy mountains. Once in the woods he gets caught by the Devil and finds himself in Hell. There he finds a crystal, will it be the key to another life?

Thoughts on our Planet

Daisy Wilkinson

Do you care about pollution in the air?
Sometimes the world just isn't fair.

Less violence. Just a bit more peace.
Save bees and plant more trees.

Covid is a dread.
Try turning eco instead.

The only war we need is to help the poor.
A rule for life is that less is more.

Three Screams

Amina Ali

It was the night of the Halloween party. A friendship group of three girls decided to dress as Power Puff Girls. Not very scary, but fun anyway. Little did they know it would make them an easy target.

The party was well under way and the girls went to the toilet to fix their hair and gossip. Suddenly there was a big bang and the music stopped. Everyone ran outside but the girls stayed inside the bathroom. They waited for hours, and everyone had disappeared. There was no escape from the rubble and mess. The girls started to call out for help, but nobody came. The oldest and bravest of the girls went towards the door and prised it open.

'Ahh!!' she screamed. A bullet had found her head.

Eight Six-Word Stories

Man becomes dad. Baby wasn't his.
Isaac Kuyateh

One million lost. Police find suspect.
Sebastian Ward

Imaginary monsters were making eyeball soup.
Ruby Dunning

Sick, cough, tired, unwell, quiet... dead.
Amina Ali

Works at butchers. Bodies for sale.
Liam Woods

Haunted house. Great candy. It's May!
Amy Ortola

Guns fired, bombs dropped, friends gone.
Zakim Hanif-Thompson

Ash, death... the end of life.
William Walker

Halloween

Zakim Hanif-Thompson

Down in the woods on 31st October
The spooky stories come over.

The house is a trap.
Don't fall for that.

Don't look right into his eyes.
You will be traumatised.

There will be no escape
Bound with duct tape.

They'll turn you into a ghost, just like me.
I promise it will be the scariest thing you will ever see.

Roller Coaster

Scarlett Oeser

Sitting on the edge of my seat, waiting for the roller coaster to take off. I'm petrified as my hands tightly clutch the bar. The carriage starts to go up and I'm really out of my comfort zone now.

My first time on a roller coaster and I don't know what all the fuss is about.

It goes up and then we come down. It flies round and round and my stomach feels like it's falling out of my mouth. I could live without this happening again.

Dear Mr Wyke

Amy Ortola

You are amazing.

You might not know me, but I know you.
A kind person, that is you.
All you say is true.
That is what I think of you, thank you.

Thanks for the corner shops, the parks,
The good people, the food,
And for not wanting to hide under a hoodie.

If you could talk, you'd say,
'You're all welcome, no matter who you are.'
And I'd say,
'Thank you.'

The Ice is Melting

Grace Duffy

I woke up this morning still half asleep
Threw open the curtains to look out on the street.

Just wait a minute. What's that over there?
Down in the garden there was a massive polar bear.

I opened the window and shouted 'Oi! You shouldn't be here.'
He explained the ice is melting year by year.

'The ice is melting, didn't you know?
So, me and my family have nowhere to go.'

'Sorry,' I said. I answered with shame.
'But if we all pull together, we can turn around your pain.'

So, whoever reads this, help save your planet.

Hostages

Heidi Hargreaves

We received a call, a complaint about children screaming in a flat on the outskirts of town. A group of us were sent to investigate.

When we got there, we entered the flat by kicking the door down. I saw a child in the corner with bruises down her arms. The man was holding a whip. I grabbed the whip from him and we made an arrest.

After searching the house, we found wallets, guns and drugs. We found the other children hidden in the basement.

Your Local Rappa

Isaac Kuyateh

Yo, yo!
What's going on, you hobo?

I'm off to Tesco.
Do you want a Dorito?
Gonna have some Skittles cos I wanna taste the rainbow.

I know some people are psycho.
My favourite fruit is a mango.

Wagwan Joe,
I like your Afro.

Seven Six-Word Stories

Safari went wrong. Tiger was full.
Liam Woods

Mirrored ghost seen during maths class.
Sebastian Ward

Maid poisoned drink, master found dead.
Georgia Bentley

World is fading. People are erasing.
Amina Ali

Studies at university, becomes a millionaire.
Preston Simpson

Lights flickered. Boy hidden. Kidnapper arrived.
William Walker

Blood on wedding dress. Accidents happen.
Grace Duffy

The Disappearance

Oscar Wang

The children couldn't resist going to the abandoned school even though they knew they shouldn't.

As they explored the empty rooms, it got creepier and creepier. It was as if someone was following them but there was nobody there, just a draught blowing down the corridors.

As the children turned to leave, the doors slammed shut.

'Do you want to play a game?' came a voice from the darkness.

'No, we want to go home,' screamed the children.

They never went home again.

A year later, a boy felt the urge to visit the school. All was fine until he decided to shout out, 'Hello.' A draught appeared from nowhere again, and the boy vanished into thin air.

Mum's Dress

Isaac Kuyateh

Mum's dress so long and neat,
Mum's dress smells so sweet.

Mum's dress is oh so white,
Mum's dress always bright.

Mum's dress pulled over her head,
Mum's dress draped over the bed.

Mum's dress now old and thin,
Mum's dress now in the bin.

Unsolved Murder

Amy Ortola

It was 2 a.m. on the 16th January 2019, and police sirens could be heard across the city. Five police vans, a helicopter and a whole team of detectives had been called to a mass shooting at Sunset Hotel.

Hotel guests were petrified. The police ran up the stairs to the crime scene on the fifth floor. Forensic samples were collected from the dead bodies strewn everywhere.

The police thought that they had it all under control and that the case would be solved in three to five months.

Three years later, and it's still unsolved. The murderer remains at large and could be standing right next to you. Don't trust anyone.

Eight Six-Word Stories

My phone's ringing. It's him again.
Lexi Preston

Knife crime! Police. Bodies. Blood. Tears.
Amina Ali

Kitten in a bag, car coming.
Heidi Hargreaves

First human on earth, monkey evolution.
Sebastian Ward

Visited the library. Opened a curse.
Georgia Bentley

Fish got 'fishnapped'. Tea is gone.
Leo Richmond

Discovered new virus. Human life gone.
Grace Duffy

No money. Crime... Stuck in cell.
Amy Atter

Dear Mr Wyke

Georgia Bentley

Dear Mr Wyke,
You make my life what it is. You are kind and generous and amazing, but...
You have too much damned rain,
More storms than sun.
You have a nice warm jacket but the rest of us don't.

But, Mr Wyke,
I thank you for eleven years' worth of memories and probably many more. I will never forget.

Mr Wyke,
I like it when you bless us with extra money. (My mum once found £5 on the floor, and an extra £10 in the cash machine.)

And, Mr Wyke,
I know you would want to protect us if any trouble came our way.

Every morning, Mr Wyke,
You say good morning when I'm on my way to school and I say it back to you.

I love you, Mr Wyke, even though it rains a lot!

Save Our Planet

Zoe Makhubelo

Do you want to save the Earth?
Eat less meat.

Do you want to save the Earth?
Use less plastic.

Do you want to save the Earth?
Look after our oceans.

Do you want to save the Earth?
Let's all work together.

Spooky Saturday

Amy Atter

The Earth was spinning on its own axis, faster and faster. The wind was howling, throwing leaves and debris at the girl's bedroom window. The house was in darkness and freezing cold. Strange creaking noises were coming from the attic.

What was happening? What had she done to deserve this? She just wanted a normal Saturday, watching television in her pyjamas.

Why was life so complicated?

Eight Six-Word Stories

All friends keep secrets, don't they?
Zoe Makhubelo

White wedding corpse, bride was dead.
Scarlett Oeser

No more life. Earth was scary.
Sebastian Ward

Down in the mine, what's shining?
Liam Woods

People diving. Fish hiding. Spears shoot.
Preston Simpson

Dead flowers pressed now live forever.
Grace Duffy

Saw a ghost. Didn't wake up.
Amy Atter

Dad died. Mum cried. Son hides.
Isaac Kuyateh

As

William Walker, Joel Brown and Oscar Wang

As fat as thin,
As smooth as skin.

As slow as fast,
As hurtful as the past.

As honeyed as ham,
As strong as a man.

As dark as light,
As painful as flight.

As young as old,
As timid as bold.

As high as the floor,
As open as a door.

Birthday Memories

Daisy Wilkinson

I remember it well, 31st December, my birthday. I opened my present from my mum. It was a Pandora bracelet. My favourite.

We went off to church as usual and I showed off my bracelet to everybody. I got lots of attention. Most people said that it was beautiful, although just a few made funny comments. I think they were jealous.

My grandparents bought me a River Island voucher and that made my birthday the best ever.

Good memories stay with you for ever.

Please Stop

Liam Woods

No more homelessness,
Stop them begging on their knees.

Put an end to racism,
Your colour shouldn't matter.

Call out sexism,
Who cares if you're a boy or a girl.

End discrimination,
We all have something to give.

Finally, let's try and save the planet,
Switch to electric cars.

A Sad End

Georgia Bentley

The police had wanted him for years. All evidence had been gathered and they were finally going to raid his house. His name was Big C, he was twenty-five years old with a wife and daughter. The wife was to be taken into custody and their beautiful young daughter would be taken into care.

All was expected to go smoothly, but somehow Big C knew they were after him and, when they found him, he had stopped breathing. The police would never get answers to their questions.

His wife suffered in prison, even having her face burnt with sugar and warm water yet she wouldn't tell anybody anything. The only person with answers to all the questions was the daughter. Would she tell?

Memories of Home

Amy Atter

Mr Wyke,

You have created many memories,
And will probably create many more.
A wonderful childhood like...

Going to my cousin's next door,
Visiting my nan's,
Playing in the park,
A trip to the shops,
My wonderful nursery
And lots more.

Sometimes you wear a black mask to cover up my pain,
Or a raincoat to stop the rain,
A gold chain to cheer me up,
Trainers to make me tall.

Even though I don't live with you any more,
I still call you home.

Eight Six-Word Stories

Pounce, suck, kill. Back in coffin.
Lexi Preston

In action for the last time.
Sebastian Ward

Mad librarian. Fire starts. Books gone.
Heidi Hargreaves

Pink fluffy unicorns dancing on rainbows.
Ruby Dunning

One person survives Earth's zombie apocalypse.
Sebastian Ward

A pencil, some paper, discovered words.
Joel Brown

Monster under bed. Frightened child screams!
Amy Ortola

I think this is the end.
Oscar Wang

Halloween Gone Wrong

Liam Woods

Chocolate or sweets
Haunt people.

Ogres set free.
Isolated kids.

Can we survive?
End of humanity.

Man Caught with Deadly Wolf

Scarlett Oeser

Last night, in the village of Walkby, people reported seeing a man walking what appeared to be a huge dog. Later in the night, there were reports of howling on the outskirts of the village. The howls did not belong to a dog and were more wolf-like.

The police were called along with Animal Control and they surrounded a house on the edge of the village. Police obtained entry to the house and found a man cowering in the corner, sheltering an injured wolf and its cubs. The man explained that he'd found the wolf shivering and injured and had only wanted to help.

Animal Control took the wolf away and villagers sighed in relief.

Tribute to Ronaldo

Zakim Hanif-Thompson

Ronaldo's celebrations are legendary and unforgettable:
Outstanding goal scorer,
Often man of the match.

Dedication to his sport is unrivalled.
Raw talent and hard work.

If only I had a four-leaf clover,
For only then would I receive a signed shirt!

Childhood Memories

Grace Duffy

When I was a little girl, my grandad always took me on adventures. There would be a different adventure every week. I looked forward to those times.

We used an app to go Geocaching. Every week we would look for treasure. Different people's ideas of treasure were intriguing, and it was always a challenge to think of my own treasure to replace it with.

This one particular morning seemed different. We loaded the app and drove to our destination. We got out of the car and the app directed us to a small wooden gate. We opened the gate and stepped into another world – a world of fairies and gnomes and all that was right with the world.

I'll never forget that morning.

Six-Word Biographies

AMINA ALI: Indecisive, high standards, unreasonable, amazing, fun.

AMY ATTER: Animal lover, loving friend, quiet listener.

GEORGIA BENTLEY: Kind, but don't make me mad!

JOEL BROWN: I'm a footballer and I'm smart.

GRACE DUFFY: Longish hair, plays fair, animal lover.

RUBY DUNNING: Pink fluffy unicorns and dancing rainbows.

ZAKIM HANIF-THOMPSON: Sits quietly, thinking up new stories.

HEIDI HARGREAVES: Funny, pretty, strange, shy, loyal, stubborn.

ISAAC KUYATEH: Funny, handsome, kinda smart. Big head!

ZOE MAKHUBELO: Trust issues. Weird big-headed girl.

SCARLETT OESER: Wonderful! Always girly, giggling, loving everything.

AMY ORTOLA: Short curly hair and a smile.

LEXI PRESTON: Long hair. Doesn't share. That's me!

LEO RICHMOND: Football-lover, joke-maker, friend-collector.

PRESTON SIMPSON: Loud, proud, good to be around.

WILLIAM WALKER: Strange, weird and maybe an alien.

OSCAR WANG: Funny, nice, trustworthy, kind and intelligent.

SEBASTIAN WARD: Absolutely no words can describe me.

DAISY WILKINSON: Respected, peaceful, sensitive. Fashion's my passion.

LIAM WOODS: I am smart, like an elephant.

About Nick Toczek

Born in Bradford, and still living in the city, Nick Toczek is a writer and performer who has published more than fifty books. He has also released numerous albums of both spoken word and music, and is a professional magician and puppeteer. For more information about him and his work, check out his website (www.nicktoczek.com) and his Wikipedia page.

Acknowledgements

Melanie Curtis at Avon DataSet for her overwhelming support for First Story and for giving her time in typesetting this anthology.

Vivienne Heller for copy-editing and Sally Beets for proofreading this anthology.

Lucy Dove for assisting with the cover design for this anthology.

Foysal Ali at Aquatint for printing this anthology at a discounted rate.

HRH The Duchess of Cornwall, Patron of First Story.

The Founders of First Story:
Katie Waldegrave and William Fiennes.

The Trustees of First Story:
Ed Baden-Powell (chair), Aziz Bawany, Aslan Byrne, Sophie Harrison, Sue Horner, Sarah Marshall, Bobby Nayyar, Jamie Waldegrave and Ella White.

First Story Ambassadors:
Patrice Lawrence MBE and Tracy Chevalier FRSL.

Thanks to our funders:
Jane & Peter Aitken, Amazon Literary Partnership, Authors' Licensing and Collecting Society (ALCS), Arts Council England, Tim Bevan & Amy Gadney, Fiona Byrd, The Blue Thread, Boots Charitable Trust, Fiona Byrd, Full House Literary Magazine, Garfield Weston Foundation, Goldsmith's Company Charity, John Lyons Charity, John R Murray Charitable Trust, Man Charitable Trust, Mercers' Company Charity, Paul Hamlyn Foundation, family and friends of Philip Pyke, ProWritingAid, RWHA Charity Fund, teamArchie, Wellington Management UK Foundation, Wordbank, the Friends of First Story and our regular supporters, individual donors and those who choose to remain anonymous.

Pro bono supporters and delivery partners including:
Arvon Foundation, BBC Teach, British Library, Cambridge University, Centre for Literacy in Primary Education, David Higham Associates, Driver Youth Trust, English and Media Centre, Forward Arts Foundation, Greenwich University, Hachette, Hull University, Huddersfield University, National Literacy Trust, Nottingham Trent University, Penguin Random House and Walker Books.

Most importantly we would like to thank the students, teachers and writers who have worked so hard to make First Story a success this year, as well as the many individuals and organisations (including those who we may have omitted to name) who have given their generous time, support and advice.